GREAT MINDS® WIT & WISDOM

Grade 4 Module 1:
A Great Heart

Student Edition

Table of Contents

Handout 1A: Quotations by Barnard and Confucius

Handout 2A: Heart Quotations

Handout 2B: Exemplar Essay

Handout 2C: Fluency Homework

Handout 3A: Frayer Model

Handout 4A: Evidence Organizer for a Figurative Great Heart

Handout 6A: Dr. Gross Quotation

Handout 6B: Evidence Organizer for Dr. Gross

Handout 7A: Active Listening Strategies

Handout 7B: *The Circulatory Story* Vocabulary

Handout 8A: Fluency Homework

Handout 9A: *The Circulatory Story* Vocabulary

Handout 9B: Evidence Organizer for Figurative Language

Handout 9C: Booklet

Handout 10A: Main Ideas in *The Circulatory Story*

Handout 10B: *The Circulatory Story* Vocabulary

Handout 12A: Fluency Homework

Handout 12B: Capitalization Practice

Handout 13A: Commas before Conjunctions Rules

Handout 13B: Commas before Conjunctions Practice

Handout 14A: Compound Sentences

Handout 16A: A Healthy Heart

Handout 16B: Heart Diagram

Handout 17A: Evidence Organizer for *The Circulatory Story*

Handout 18A: Fluency Homework

Handout 19A: Order of Adjectives

Handout 23A: Fluency Homework

Handout 29A: Evidence Organizer for *Love That Dog*

Handout 30A: Poetry Performance Exit Ticket

Handout 31A: Socratic Seminar Self-Assessment

Handout 31B: Style and Conventions Checklist

Handout 32A: End-of-Module Evidence Organizer

Handout 32B: Essay Planner for the End-of-Module Task

Volume of Reading Reflection Questions

Wit & Wisdom Parent Tip Sheet

Name: _____

Date: _____

Handout 1A: Quotations by Barnard and Confucius

Directions: Silently reread the quotations below:

"It is infinitely better to transplant a **heart** than to bury it to be devoured by worms."

–Christiaan Barnard, the first cardiovascular
surgeon to transplant a human heart

"Wherever you go, go with all your **heart**."

–Confucius, a Chinese philosopher

Directions: Annotate the two quotations in the following ways:

- Mark **?** for questions.

- Circle unknown words.

- Write observations in the margins.

- Write an F or L to show whether the speaker is using the word *heart* figuratively or literally.

Name: _____

Date: _____

Handout 2A: Heart Quotations

Directions: Use these quotations to explore the difference between a literal and a figurative great heart.

"It is infinitely better to transplant a **heart** than to bury it to be devoured by worms."
–Christiaan Barnard

"Wherever you go, go with all your **heart**." –Confucius

Who Said It?	The Quotation
Helen Keller, author, teacher who overcame being both blind and deaf	The best and most beautiful things in the world cannot be seen or even touched–they must be felt with the heart.
Michael Miller, MD, F.A.C.C., Center for Preventive Cardiology at the University of Maryland Medical Center	The recommendation for a healthy heart may one day be exercise, eat right, and laugh a few times a day.
Nelson Mandela, an anti-apartheid leader, South Africa's first black president	A good head and a good heart are always a formidable combination.
Anne Frank, a young Jewish Holocaust victim, kept a diary	Despite everything, I believe that people are really good at heart.
NOVA website	Your heart beats about 100,000 times in one day and about 35 million times in a year.
John Muir, a Scottish-American naturalist who advocated for national parks	Keep close to Nature's heart...and break clear away, once in a while, and climb a mountain or spend a week in the woods. Wash your spirit clean.
Anonymous, a veteran trapeze artist	Throw your heart over the bars and your body will follow.
Bill Nye, "The Science Guy"	Your heart is a pump. It pushes blood all over your body.

Who Said It?	The Quotation
Theodore Roosevelt, 26th U.S. president	I think there is only one quality worse than hardness of heart and that is softness of head.
Chinese proverb	If I keep a green bough in my heart, then the singing bird will come.
Angelique Tuyishimere, age 6, suffers from chronic heart condition	If they would fix my heart, I would thank God.
Thomas Eakins, an American Realist painter, portraitist, and sculptor who shifted American art's focus from landscape art to people	If America is to produce great painters, [young artists should] remain in America to peer deeper into the heart of American life.
Graham London, British cyclist	A healthy heart keeps you strong—then you can fight for those who can't.
Eleanor Roosevelt, first lady of the United States	To handle yourself, use your head: To handle others, use your heart.
Clara Barton, Civil War nurse, "Angel of the Battlefield," and founder of the American Red Cross	If I were to speak of war, it would not be to show you the glories of conquering armies but the mischief and misery they strew in their tracks; and how, while they marched on with tread of iron and plumes proudly tossing in the breeze, someone must follow closely in their steps, crouching to the earth, toiling in the rain and darkness, shelterless themselves, with no thought of pride or glory, fame or praise, or reward; hearts breaking with pity, faces bathed in tears and hands in blood. This is the side which history never shows.

Name: _____

Date: _____

Handout 2B: Exemplar Essay

Directions: Read the following essay.

Have you ever really thought about what your coach or piano teacher means when they say, "Come on! I want to see you put your heart into it!"? The word *heart* is an interesting word because it can be used both literally and figuratively when we speak, when we read, or when we write. When the word is used literally, it refers to the human heart, that organ that beats as it pumps blood to all of your other body parts. When the word is used figuratively, it refers to the emotion that shows caring, effort, and involvement in other people's lives and your own.

Sometimes, the word *heart* is used literally. Christiaan Barnard, a South African heart surgeon, said, "It is infinitely better to transplant a heart than to bury it to be devoured by worms." He was saying that when you die, it is much better to donate your heart to a living person than to bury it. In this quotation, Barnard was using the word *heart* literally to refer to the organ in a person's body. He wanted people to reuse their real, beating hearts to save another person's life.

At other times, *heart* is used figuratively. For example, when Confucius said, "Wherever you go, go with all your heart," he wasn't talking about the heart that beats inside your body. He was saying that a person has a choice of taking his heart with him when he goes somewhere. For example, when a student enters a classroom on the first day of school, he can choose to do his essay or his math assignment with all his heart or with very little effort invested. If Confucius was talking about the literal heart, he would have been saying something very silly, like a person had the option of taking his physical heart out of his body when he was going somewhere or doing something. In saying that we need to go somewhere with our full effort and emotional involvement, with our whole heart, Confucius was using the word *heart* in a figurative way.

In conclusion, the word *heart* can be used both literally, as in Christiaan Barnard's quotation, and figuratively, as in Confucius' quotation. It is up to the reader to put his or her whole heart into the reading to determine the speaker's intended meaning.

Name: _____

Date: _____

Handout 2C: Fluency Homework

Directions:

1. Day 1: Read the text carefully and annotate to help you read fluently.

2. Each day:

   a. Practice reading the text aloud three to five times.

   b. Evaluate your progress by placing a checkmark in the appropriate, unshaded box.

   c. Ask someone (adult or peer) to listen and evaluate you as well.

3. Last day: Answer the self-reflection questions at the end.

Helen Keller said, "The best and most beautiful things in the world cannot be seen or even touched—they must be felt with the heart."

Nelson Mandela said, "A good head and a good heart are always a formidable combination."

John Muir said, "Keep close to Nature's heart...and break clear away, once in a while, and climb a mountain or spend a week in the woods. Wash your spirit clean."

Eleanor Roosevelt said, "To handle yourself, use your head; to handle others, use your heart."

Student Performance Checklist:	Day 1		Day 2		Day 3		Day 4	
	You	Listener*	You	Listener*	You	Listener*	You	Listener*
Accurately read the passage three to five times.								
Read with appropriate phrasing and pausing.								
Read with appropriate expression.								
Read articulately at a good pace and an audible volume.								

*Adult or peer

Self-reflection: What choices did you make when deciding how to read this passage, and why? What would you like to improve on or try differently next time? (*Thoughtfully answer these questions in the space below. Use a separate sheet of paper if necessary to complete your reflection.*)

Name: _____

Date: _____

Handout 3A: Frayer Model

Directions: Complete this chart to understand the word *greathearted*.

Definition:	Characteristics:

Word:

greathearted

Examples:	Non-Examples:

Name: _____

Date: _____

Handout 4A: Evidence Organizer for a Figurative Great Heart

Directions: Choose the best evidence to support your focus statement. Write brief notes in the boxes. Remember to only write notes that support your focus.

How does someone show a great heart, figuratively?			
Focus Statement:			
Context Why is this person famous?	**Evidence** What details support the focus? Quote or paraphrase.	**Source** What is the source of the evidence? List title and page number.	**Elaboration/Explanation** How does this show great heart?

Context	Evidence	Source	Elaboration/Explanation
Why is this person famous?	What details support the focus? Quote or paraphrase.	What is the source of the evidence? List title and page number.	How does this show great heart?

Name: _____

Date: _____

Handout 6A: Dr. Gross Quotation

Directions: Read the following quotation and then paraphrase each section as it is listed below.

"I never enter the lecture-room without a deep sense of the responsibility of my office—without a sense that I have a solemn duty to perform—and that upon what I may utter during the hour may depend the happiness or misery of hundreds, if not thousands, of human beings. Nothing was more offensive to me than applause when I entered the amphitheater, and I never permitted it after the first lecture. I always said, 'Gentlemen, such a noise is more befitting a theater or a circus than a temple dedicated...to almighty God, for the study of disease and accident, and your preparation for the great duties of your profession. There is something awfully solemn in a profession that deals with life and death; and I desire...to impress upon your minds its sacred and responsible character."

(Section 1) "I never enter the lecture-room without a deep sense of the responsibility of my office—without a sense that I have a solemn duty to perform—and that upon what I may utter during the hour may depend the happiness or misery of hundreds, if not thousands, of human beings..."

Directions: Rewrite section 1 in your own words.

_____

_____

_____

_____

(Section 2) "Nothing was more offensive to me than applause when I entered the amphitheater, and I never permitted it after the first lecture. I always said, 'Gentlemen, such a noise is more befitting a theater or a circus than a temple dedicated...to almighty God, for the study of disease and accident, and your preparation for the great duties of your profession.'"

Directions: Rewrite section 2 in your own words.

_____

_____

_____

_____

(Section 3) "There is something awfully solemn in a profession that deals with life and death; and I desire...to impress upon your minds its sacred and responsible character."

Directions: Rewrite section 3 in your own words.

_____

_____

_____

_____

Name: _____

Date: _____

Handout 6B: Evidence Organizer for Dr. Gross

Directions: Choose the best evidence to support your focus statement that Dr. Gross showed great heart. Write brief notes in the boxes. Remember to only write notes that support your focus.

How does someone show a great heart, figuratively?			
Focus Statement: Dr. Gross was an important historical figure who showed great heart through...			
Context	Evidence	Source	Elaboration/Explanation
Why is this person famous?	What details support the focus? Quote or paraphrase.	What is the source of the evidence?	How does this show great heart?

Context	Evidence	Source	Elaboration/Explanation
Why is this person famous?	What details support the focus? Quote or paraphrase.	What is the source of the evidence?	How does this show great heart?

Name: _____

Date: _____

Handout 7A: Active Listening Strategies

Directions: Use the following ideas to help you concentrate when you are actively listening.

I am actively listening when I do the following:

- Sit up and look at the speaker

- Nod my head in agreement with something the speaker said

- Make eye contact with the speaker

- Read along in my own book when someone is reading aloud

- Jot down questions or comments I have about something the speaker said or read

- Wait for the right time to share my thoughts without interrupting someone else

- Keep my comments or questions on topic

- Ask clarifying questions

Name: _____

Date: _____

Handout 7B: *The Circulatory Story* Vocabulary

Directions: Study the definitions and then draw and color a picture to help you remember what each word means.

Word	Definition	Illustration
circulatory	Related to the circulation of blood	
component	A part of a larger object or system	
hemoglobin	A protein found in red blood cells that transports, or carries, oxygen	

transport	To carry something from one place to another	
cell	The smallest, functioning unit of a living organism	
plasma	The liquid part of the blood; 90 percent of plasma is water	
pericardium	A protective sac that encloses the heart	

Name: _____

Date: _____

Handout 8A: Fluency Homework

Directions:

1. Day 1: Read the text carefully and annotate to help you read fluently.

2. Each day:

   a. Practice reading the text aloud three to five times.

   b. Evaluate your progress by placing a checkmark in the appropriate, unshaded box.

   c. Ask someone (adult or peer) to listen and evaluate you as well.

3. Last day: Answer the self-reflection questions at the end.

Arteries are big. All arteries have thick, elastic walls. These walls have three layers, each with lots of give so they can expand as blood passes through them. The artery you're traveling in as you leave the left ventricle is called the aorta. It's the biggest artery in the whole body. It's an important one, too, because all blood travels through it before heading off to other places in the body.

As you travel through the aorta, you'll notice that it forms an arch. Like subway tunnels, three blood vessels branch off the top of the arch. These three blood vessels are arteries that carry blood to the head, neck, and arms. The aorta continues on, however, carrying blood downward. The blood traveling through the aorta will eventually branch off to reach the rest of the body, including the lungs, kidneys, stomach, intestines, and legs.

Corcoran, Mary K., and Jef Czekaj. *The Circulatory Story*. Charlesbridge Publishing, 2010, pp. 16-17.

Student Performance Checklist:	Day 1		Day 2		Day 3		Day 4	
	You	Listener*	You	Listener*	You	Listener*	You	Listener*
Accurately read the passage three to five times.								
Read with appropriate phrasing and pausing.								
Read with appropriate expression.								
Read articulately at a good pace and an audible volume.								

*Adult or peer

Self-reflection: What choices did you make when deciding how to read this passage, and why? What would you like to improve on or try differently next time? (*Thoughtfully answer these questions in the space below. Use a separate sheet of paper if necessary to complete your reflection.*)

Name: _____

Date: _____

Handout 9A: *The Circulatory Story* Vocabulary

Directions: Study the definitions and then draw and color a picture to help you remember what each word means.

Word	Definition	Illustration
septum	The membrane that separates the left and the right sides of the heart	
atrium	One of the top two chambers, or rooms, of the heart that receives blood from veins	
ventricle	One of the two bottom chambers of the heart that receives blood from the atrium and sends it out of the heart through an artery	

chamber	A "room" in the heart	
mitral valve	A heart valve located between the left atrium and the left ventricle	
aortic valve	A heart valve located between the left ventricle and the aorta	

Name: _____

Date: _____

Handout 9B: Evidence Organizer for Figurative Language

Directions: Choose the best evidence to answer the question. Write brief notes in the boxes. Remember to only write notes that support your focus statement.

How does figurative language convey meaning in *The Circulatory Story?*			
Focus Statement:			
Context What is being described?	**Evidence** What does the text say? What is being compared?	**Source** What is the source of the evidence? List title and page number.	**Elaboration/Explanation** What does this help us understand?

Context	Evidence	Source	Elaboration/Explanation
What is being described?	What does the text say? What is being compared?	What is the source of the evidence? List title and page number.	What does this help us understand?

Name: _____

Date: _____

Handout 9C: Booklet

Directions: Complete this booklet to show how the figurative language in *The Circulatory Story* provides meaning to the text.

Question: How does figurative language convey meaning in *The Circulatory Story*?

Title _____

_____

_____

_____

_____

Name: _____

Date: _____

Handout 10A: Main Ideas in *The Circulatory Story*

Directions: Read the bullets and decide what the big idea is for that section of text. Write the big idea in the box above the set of bullets.

```
┌─────────────────────────────────────────────────────────────────┐
│                                                                   │
│                                                                   │
│                                                                   │
│                                                                   │
└─────────────────────────────────────────────────────────────────┘
```

Page 11 Details

- Blood flows in and out with each heartbeat.

- The chambers squeeze and then relax.

- The chambers send blood through the heart and into blood vessels.

- Each atrium and ventricle squeezes.

```
┌─────────────────────────────────────────────────────────────────┐
│                                                                   │
│                                                                   │
│                                                                   │
└─────────────────────────────────────────────────────────────────┘
```

Pages 12–13 Details

- The valves open when the squeezes happen.

- Valves keep blood flowing in the right direction.

- When the left atrium squeezes (contracts), the mitral valve opens.

- When the blood flows into the left ventricle, the valve closes.

- The left ventricle contracts and pushes blood out to the rest of the body.

Pages 14–15 Details

- The left ventricle is a strong muscle.

- It pushes blood through the aortic valve into the blood vessels.

- There are 60,000 miles of blood vessels in the human body.

- The arteries carry blood away from the heart. (**A**rteries = **A**way)

- The veins carry blood to the heart.

- Capillaries connect arteries and veins. (**C**apillaries = **C**onnect)

Name: _____

Date: _____

Handout 10B: *The Circulatory Story* Vocabulary

Directions: Read each word and its definition from *The Circulatory Story*. Draw and color a picture to help you remember the meaning of each word.

Word	Definition	Illustration
valve	A flap that opens and closes to allow blood to flow through the arteries in one direction	
artery	A vessel that carries blood away from the heart	

capillary	A vessel that connects arteries and veins	
vein	A vessel that carries blood to the heart	

Name: _____

Date: _____

Handout 12A: Fluency Homework

Directions:

1. Day 1: Read the text carefully and annotate to help you read fluently.

2. Each day:

   a. Practice reading the text aloud three to five times.

   b. Evaluate your progress by placing a checkmark in the appropriate, unshaded box.

   c. Ask someone (adult or peer) to listen and evaluate you as well.

3. Last day: Answer the self-reflection questions at the end.

Oh, no ... look at that sticky gunk on the walls of this coronary artery. It's plaque—no, not the kind that can build up on your teeth. The plaque in arteries is a fatty substance. An unhealthy diet, especially lots of fatty foods, can cause plaque to build up in people's arteries, which can lead to a clog in a coronary artery. Think of the pipes below your kitchen sink. If too much gunk builds up, water can't pass through the pipes. Then it's time to get the plunger.

Adults with lots of plaque in their coronary arteries are at risk of having a heart attack. Some of this nasty plaque may prevent blood from reaching heart cells. Without oxygen, these cells become damaged. When this happens, a doctor has to unclog that artery.

Treating your heart well helps prevent heart trouble. Two heart-smart ideas are to eat right and to exercise. This way, the heart can be buff and healthy. This advice is straight from the heart!

Corcoran, Mary K., and Jef Czekaj. *The Circulatory Story*. Charlesbridge Publishing, 2010, pp. 36-37.

Student Performance Checklist:	Day 1		Day 2		Day 3		Day 4	
	You	Listener*	You	Listener*	You	Listener*	You	Listener*
Accurately read the passage three to five times.								
Read with appropriate phrasing and pausing.								
Read with appropriate expression.								
Read articulately at a good pace and an audible volume.								

*Adult or peer

Self-reflection: What choices did you make when deciding how to read this passage, and why? What would you like to improve on or try differently next time? (*Thoughtfully answer these questions in the space below. Use a separate sheet of paper if necessary to complete your reflection.*)

Name: _____

Date: _____

Handout 12B: Capitalization Practice

Directions: Read the following paragraph. If words are not capitalized, draw two underlines under the first letter. Then, rewrite the word above the sentence.

grand central station is a train station in new york city, new york. it was built in the early

1900s for the purpose of bringing people into new york to work, shop, and play. the

structure is technically called grand central terminal. in addition, it has been an art gallery

and host to musical performances. the elegance of the architecture makes it a sight to see

for visitors every day. it is a beautiful and majestic landmark in new york. new york city is

known as "the city that never sleeps," a quote from a song by frank sinatra titled "new york,

new york." the city continues to bustle with activity, thanks to grand central terminal!

Name: _____

Date: _____

Handout 13A: Commas before Conjunctions Rules

Directions: Complete this chart by filling in the information in the last two columns.

Use of a Comma	What do I notice that is the same in these sentences? Why is a comma used in each sentence?	What is the rule?
"This left atrium is a nice place to visit, but don't get too comfortable here." (11)		
"Yes, it goes to the heart's left side, and blood will now be pumped out of the left ventricle and on to the body's cells." (34)		
"It's the shortest circuit in the body, but it's important because it supplies the heart itself with blood." (35)		

Name: _____

Date: _____

Handout 13B: Commas before Conjunctions Practice

Directions: Read both sentences and make them a compound sentence by adding a comma and a conjunction (*and, or,* or *but*).

1. The heart will beat faster if you exercise. It will be slower when you stop.

   Compound sentence:

   _____

   _____

   _____

2. People like to exercise to have a healthy heart. Some are more serious about exercise than others.

   Compound sentence:

   _____

   _____

   _____

3. Jennifer, you may want to join the volleyball team. You may want to join the basketball team.

   Compound sentence:

   _____

   _____

   _____

4. Mom will pick up Kanasha after school. She will pick up Tyrone after Kanasha.

   Compound sentence:

   _____

   _____

   _____

Name: _____

Date: _____

Handout 14A: Compound Sentences

Directions: Combine two sentences and rewrite below into one compound sentence using the conjunctions *and, or,* or *but.*

1. Exercise is important in having a healthy heart.

   Some people don't take care of themselves.

   _____

   _____

   _____

2. Eating fruits and vegetables in a healthy diet is important.

   They make you not only healthy but feel better.

   _____

   _____

   _____

3. To get fit, you can exercise at home by yourself.

   Some people would rather exercise with a group of people.

   _____

   _____

   _____

4. Restaurants have healthy choices on their menus.

   You have to really study them to know which foods are healthy and which are not.

   _____

   _____

   _____

Name: _____

Date: _____

Handout 16A: A Healthy Heart

Directions: Read each statement and finish the inference about a healthy heart. Reread the pages in *The Circulatory Story* to help you.

Page 13: If serious valve problems cause the heart to work harder, then **a healthy heart**

_____

_____

Page 31: If exercise causes the heart to send more blood and oxygen, then **a healthy heart**

_____

_____

Page 36: If blocked coronary arteries cause heart attacks, then **a healthy heart**

_____

_____

Page 37: If eating fatty foods causes arteries to clog up with plaque, then **a healthy heart**

_____

_____

Name: _____

Date: _____

Handout 16B: Heart Diagram

Directions: Label the diagram of the heart with the words listed here, using *The Circulatory Story*, pages 9–11, as a reference.

Right atrium

Left atrium

Right ventricle

Left ventricle

Mitral valve

Aortic valve

Tricuspid valve

Pulmonary veins

Pulmonary arteries

Aorta

Superior Vena Cava

Inferior Vena Cava

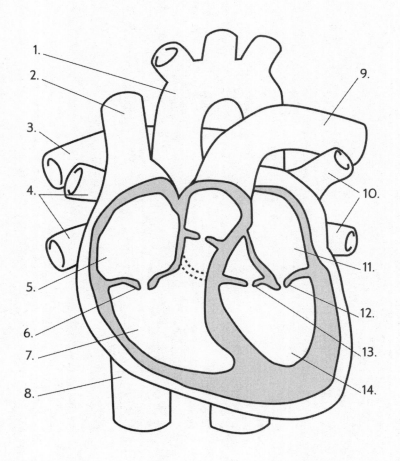

Handout 17A: Evidence Organizer for *The Circulatory Story*

Directions: Write a focus statement to answer the Focusing Question. Then, gather evidence to support your focus about a literal great heart.

Focusing Question: *What is a great heart, literally?*			
Focus Statement:			

Context	Evidence	Source	Elaboration/Explanation
To what part of the human heart is this related?	What is a great heart, literally?	What is the source of the evidence? List title and page number.	Why is this important?
		The Circulatory Story, 12–13	

Context	Evidence	Source	Elaboration/Explanation
To what part of the human heart is this related?	What is a great heart, literally?	What is the source of the evidence? List title and page number.	Why is this important?
		The Circulatory Story, 31	
		The Circulatory Story, 36–37	
		The Circulatory Story, 37	

Name: _____

Date: _____

Handout 18A: Fluency Homework

Directions:

1. Day 1: Read aloud the text of "Stopping by Woods on a Snowy Evening" by Robert Frost. A copy of the poem can be found online: **http://witeng.link/0663**.

2. Each day:

   a. Practice reading the text aloud three to five times.

   b. Evaluate your progress by placing a checkmark in the appropriate, unshaded box.

   c. Ask someone (adult or peer) to listen and evaluate you as well.

3. Last day: Answer the self-reflection questions at the end.

Student Performance Checklist:	Day 1		Day 2		Day 3		Day 4	
	You	Listener*	You	Listener*	You	Listener*	You	Listener*
Accurately read the passage three to five times.								
Read with appropriate phrasing and pausing.								
Read with appropriate expression.								
Read articulately at a good pace and an audible volume.								

*Adult or peer

Self-reflection: What choices did you make when deciding how to read this passage, and why? What would you like to improve on or try differently next time? (*Thoughtfully answer these questions in the space below.*)

Name: _____

Date: _____

Handout 19A: Order of Adjectives

Directions: Complete the following chart about adjectives.

Adjective/Type	Adjective/Type	Adjective/Type	Noun	Are they in the same order as anchor chart?
Example Little (Size)	Red (Color)		Hen	Yes

Overall, does the anchor chart prove to be true in today's findings? _____

Does your small group recommend adjustments to the anchor chart? _____

If so, what changes?

_____

_____

_____

Name: _____

Date: _____

Handout 23A: Fluency Homework

Directions:

For this round of fluency practice, select a poem of your choice to read. You may want to read a poem for two voices with a partner.

1. Day 1: Read the text carefully and annotate to help you read fluently.

2. Each day:

   a. Practice reading the text aloud three to five times.

   b. Evaluate your progress by placing a checkmark in the appropriate, unshaded box.

   c. Ask someone (adult or peer) to listen and evaluate you as well.

3. Last day: Answer the self-reflection questions at the end.

You will read your poem for the class on the last day!

Student Performance Checklist:	Day 1		Day 2		Day 3		Day 4	
	You	Listener*	You	Listener*	You	Listener*	You	Listener*
Accurately read the passage three to five times.								
Read with appropriate phrasing and pausing.								
Read with appropriate expression.								
Read articulately at a good pace and an audible volume.								

*Adult or peer

Self-reflection: What choices did you make when deciding how to read this passage, and why? What would you like to improve on or try differently next time? *(Thoughtfully answer these questions in the space below.)*

Name: _____

Date: _____

Handout 29A: Evidence Organizer for *Love That Dog*

Directions: Complete this organizer with information from *Love That Dog*.

How does a character in *Love That Dog* show characteristics of great heart (generous, courageous, heroic, noble)?			
Character:			
Context	**Evidence** List details from the text. Quote or paraphrase.	**Source** What is the source of the evidence? List title and page number.	**Elaboration/Explanation** Explain or give more information about what the details mean or make you think.

Context	Evidence	Source	Elaboration/Explanation
	List details from the text. Quote or paraphrase.	What is the source of the evidence? List title and page number.	Explain or give more information about what the details mean or make you think.

Name: _____

Date: _____

Handout 30A: Poetry Performance Exit Ticket

Directions: Complete the following with "Stars" (positive statements) and "Stairs" (things to improve upon).

Name:

STARS:	STAIRS:

Name: _____

Date: _____

Handout 31A: Socratic Seminar Self-Assessment

Directions: Complete this chart by using one of the letters below in the middle column to describe how often you performed the described action. In the last column, explain why you selected the letter you did.

A = I always did that.

S = I sometimes did that.

N = I'll do that next time.

Expectation	Evaluation (A, S, N)	Evidence: Why did you choose that rating?
I came to the seminar prepared and used my work as I participated in the seminar.		
I followed our class rules and expectations for the seminar, including any specific role I was assigned.		
I asked and answered questions that made our discussion clearer and linked others' ideas together.		
I explained my own ideas using the connections I made from listening to others.		

Expectation	Evaluation (A, S, N)	Evidence: Why did you choose that rating?
I used at least two vocabulary words from this module.		
I provided evidence from the texts in this module to support my points.		

Name: _____

Date: _____

Handout 31B: Style and Conventions Checklist

Directions: Use this checklist to be sure you used these items correctly.

	Self	Teacher
Style		
I use simple and compound sentences.		
I use vocabulary words that are appropriate to the topic.		
I order adjectives correctly.		
Conventions		
I use correct capitalization.		
I use correct punctuation with compound sentences.		
I use correct punctuation when quoting a speaker.		
I use correct punctuation when citing a text.		

Name: _____

Date: _____

Handout 32A: End-of-Module Evidence Organizer

Directions: Complete the following Evidence Organizer with evidence from the module texts.

What does it mean to have a great heart, literally and figuratively?

- Use evidence from the texts we have read to support your ideas.

- Choose evidence from your notes about what makes a great heart, literally, and record it on a yellow Evidence Organizer.

- Choose evidence from your notes about what makes a great heart, figuratively, and record it on a blue Evidence Organizer.

Context	Evidence	Source	Elaboration/Explanation
	Quote or paraphrase.	What is the source of the evidence? List title and page number.	Why is the evidence important?

Context	Evidence	Source	Elaboration/Explanation
	Quote or paraphrase.	What is the source of the evidence? List title and page number.	Why is the evidence important?

Name: _____

Date: _____

Handout 32B: Essay Planner for the End-of-Module Task

Directions: Use this planner to help you develop and organize your ideas for your End-of-Module Task response.

First Paragraph: Introduction

Hook **(H)** **(RED)**	How will you "hook" your audience, or catch their attention? You could ask a question, share an interesting detail, or tell a brief story.
Introduce **(I)** **(RED)**	Introduce the topic of "great heart." Provide any necessary background information or context for your topic.

Focus Statement (GREEN)	Make your focus statement.
	Point 1–(statement about literal great heart)

	Point 2–(statement about figurative great heart)

Name: _____

Date: _____

Supporting Paragraph 1–Point 1: What it means to have a great heart, literally

Topic Statement (To S) (YELLOW)	State your point about what it means to have a great heart, literally:
Evidence (E) (YELLOW)	Cite evidence that develops Point 1, your statement about literal great heart:
Elaboration (E) (YELLOW)	Explain how the evidence develops Point 1:

Concluding Statement (C) (YELLOW)	Close your paragraph:

Supporting Paragraph 2—Point 2: What it means to have a great heart, figuratively

Topic Statement (To S) (BLUE)	Transition from your last point, and state your second point about what it means to have a figurative great heart: (Transition word suggestions: *in addition, even if, however, on the other hand, also, another, whether or not*)
Evidence (E) (BLUE)	Cite evidence that develops Point 2:

Name: _____

Date: _____

Elaboration (E) (BLUE)	Explain how the evidence develops Point 2, your statement about figurative great heart:
Concluding Statement (C) (BLUE)	Close your paragraph:

Last Paragraph: Conclusion

Conclusion (C) (GREEN)	Review your focus statement. Explain "so what"–why does having a great heart matter?

Name: _____

Date: _____

Volume of Reading Reflection Questions

Grade 4 Module 1: *A Great Heart*

Student Name: _____

Text: _____

Author: _____

Topic: _____

Genre/type of book: _____

Directions: After reading a text, share what you have learned about the heart as an organ or as a symbol of caring.

1. Wonder: What drew you to this text? Before reading, did you think the book would tell more about the heart as an organ or as a symbol of caring? Explain why.

2. Organize: Summarize the main ideas of the text.

3. Organize: What vocabulary, scientific knowledge, or historical background is needed to understand this book?

4. Reveal: How does the author make the reading about the heart or having a heart interesting? Name at least two techniques the author uses.

5. Reveal: Name two ways the author communicates important ideas about the heart or having a heart.

6. Distill: What new knowledge about the heart or having a heart did you gain from this book? Provide at least three new facts you learned.

7. Distill: In what new ways does the story support the idea of the heart as a metaphor? What does the book show about how individuals can show "heart"?

8. Know: How does this text add to your knowledge about the ideas discussed in the module?

9. Know: What new insight do you have about how the heart functions or why the heart is seen as a symbol of caring?

10. Would you recommend this book to another student interested in learning about the heart or reading stories about people who demonstrate "heart"? Why or why not?

WIT & WISDOM PARENT TIP SHEET

WHAT IS MY GRADE 4 STUDENT LEARNING IN MODULE 1?

Wit & Wisdom is our English curriculum. It builds knowledge of key topics in history, science, and literature through the study of excellent texts. By reading and responding to stories and nonfiction texts, we will build knowledge of the following topics:

Module 1: A Great Heart

Module 2: Extreme Settings

Module 3: The Redcoats Are Coming!

Module 4: Myth Making

In this first module, *A Great Heart*, we will examine the complexity of the human heart. Not only is the heart a biological wonder, it is also a symbol of human emotions. We will explore what it means to have a "great heart," both literally and figuratively.

OUR CLASS WILL READ THESE BOOKS AND BIOGRAPHIES:

Novel

- *Love That Dog*, Sharon Creech

Picture Book (Informational)

- *The Circulatory Story*, Mary K. Corcoran

Biographies

- Biography of Clara Barton
- Biography of Helen Keller
- Biography of Anne Frank

OUR CLASS WILL READ THESE POEMS

- "The Red Wheelbarrow," William Carlos Williams
- "Stopping by Woods on a Snowy Evening," Robert Frost
- "The Pasture," Robert Frost

- "Love That Boy," Walter Dean Myers
- "dog," Valerie Worth
- "Heart to Heart," Rita Dove
- "The Tiger," William Blake
- "Street Music," Arnold Adoff

OUR CLASS WILL EXAMINE THIS PAINTING:

- *Portrait of Dr. Samuel D. Gross (The Gross Clinic)*, Thomas Eakins

OUR CLASS WILL WATCH THIS VIDEO:

- "Exploring the Heart - The Circulatory System!"

OUR CLASS WILL ASK THESE QUESTIONS:

- How does someone show a great heart, figuratively?
- What is a great heart, literally?
- How do the characters in *Love That Dog* show characteristics of great heart?
- What does it mean to have a great heart, literally and figuratively?

QUESTION TO ASK AT HOME:

As your Grade 4 student reads, ask:

- What do you notice and wonder?

BOOKS TO READ AT HOME:

- *Clara and Davie*, Patricia Polacco
- *Clara Barton: Angel of the Battlefield*, Editors of TIME for Kids
- *Who Was Clara Barton?* Stephanie Spinner
- *Locomotion*, Jacqueline Woodson
- *The Circulatory System*, Christine Taylor-Butler
- *Phineas Gage: A Gruesome but True Story about Brain Science*, John Fleischman

IDEAS FOR TALKING ABOUT THE HEART:

When you visit the doctor together, ask:

- *What do you wonder about your own heart?*
- *What do we do to be sure we have healthy hearts?*

At home, ask: *When is a time someone in our family showed great heart?*

CREDITS

Great Minds® has made every effort to obtain permission for the reprinting of all copyrighted material. If any owner of copyrighted material is not acknowledged herein, please contact Great Minds® for proper acknowledgment in all future editions and reprints of this module.

- All material from the *Common Core State Standards for English Language Arts & Literacy in History/Social Studies, Science, and Technical Subjects* Copyright © 2010 National Governors Association Center for Best Practices and Council of Chief State School Officers. All rights reserved.

- All images are used under license from Shutterstock.com unless otherwise noted.

- The Painted Essay® is used by permission of Diana Leddy.

- Lesson 18: "The Red Wheelbarrow" by William Carlos Williams, from THE COLLECTED POEMS: VOLUME I, 1909-1939, copyright © 1938 by New Directions Publishing Corp. Reprinted by permission of New Directions Publishing Corp.

- For updated credit information, please visit **http://witeng.link/credits**.

ACKNOWLEDGMENTS

Great Minds® Staff

The following writers, editors, reviewers, and support staff contributed to the development of this curriculum.

Ann Brigham, Lauren Chapalee, Sara Clarke, Emily Climer, Lorraine Griffith, Emily Gula, Sarah Henchey, Trish Huerster, Stephanie Kane-Mainier, Lior Klirs, Liz Manolis, Andrea Minich, Lynne Munson, Marya Myers, Rachel Rooney, Aaron Schifrin, Danielle Shylit, Rachel Stack, Sarah Turnage, Michelle Warner, Amy Wierzbicki, Margaret Wilson, and Sarah Woodard.

Colleagues and Contributors

We are grateful for the many educators, writers, and subject-matter experts who made this program possible.

David Abel, Robin Agurkis, Elizabeth Bailey, Julianne Barto, Amy Benjamin, Andrew Biemiller, Charlotte Boucher, Sheila Byrd-Carmichael, Eric Carey, Jessica Carloni, Janine Cody, Rebecca Cohen, Elaine Collins, Tequila Cornelious, Beverly Davis, Matt Davis, Thomas Easterling, Jeanette Edelstein, Kristy Ellis, Moira Clarkin Evans, Charles Fischer, Marty Gephart, Kath Gibbs, Natalie Goldstein, Christina Gonzalez, Mamie Goodson, Nora Graham, Lindsay Griffith, Brenna Haffner, Joanna Hawkins, Elizabeth Haydel, Steve Hettleman, Cara Hoppe, Ashley Hymel, Carol Jago, Jennifer Johnson, Mason Judy, Gail Kearns, Shelly Knupp, Sarah Kushner, Shannon Last, Suzanne Lauchaire, Diana Leddy, David Liben, Farren Liben, Jennifer Marin, Susannah Maynard, Cathy McGath, Emily McKean, Jane Miller, Rebecca Moore, Cathy Newton, Turi Nilsson, Julie Norris, Galemarie Ola, Michelle Palmieri, Meredith Phillips, Shilpa Raman, Tonya Romayne, Emmet Rosenfeld, Jennifer Ruppel, Mike Russoniello, Deborah Samley, Casey Schultz, Renee Simpson, Rebecca Sklepovich, Amelia Swabb, Kim Taylor, Vicki Taylor, Melissa Thomson, Lindsay Tomlinson, Melissa Vail, Keenan Walsh, Julia Wasson, Lynn Welch, Yvonne Guerrero Welch, Emily Whyte, Lynn Woods, and Rachel Zindler.

Early Adopters

The following early adopters provided invaluable insight and guidance for Wit & Wisdom:

- Bourbonnais School District 53 • Bourbonnais, IL
- Coney Island Prep Middle School • Brooklyn, NY
- Gate City Charter School for the Arts • Merrimack, NH
- Hebrew Academy for Special Children • Brooklyn, NY
- Paris Independent Schools • Paris, KY
- Saydel Community School District • Saydel, IA
- Strive Collegiate Academy • Nashville, TN
- Valiente College Preparatory Charter School • South Gate, CA
- Voyageur Academy • Detroit, MI

Design Direction provided by Alton Creative, Inc.

Project management support, production design, and copyediting services provided by **ScribeConcepts.com**

Copyediting services provided by Fine Lines Editing

Product management support provided by Sandhill Consulting